Ants don't wear pants, but what if they DID?

MW00956013

© Copyright 2006 Jon Browder.

All rights reserved. No part of this publication may be reproduced, stored in a retrieval system, or transmitted, in any form or by any means, electronic, mechanical, photocopying, recording, or otherwise, without the written prior permission of the author.

Note for Librarians: a cataloguing record for this book that includes Dewey Decimal Classification and US Library of Congress numbers is available from the Library and Archives of Canada. The complete cataloguing record can be obtained from their online database at:
www.collectionscanada.ca/amicus/index-e.html
ISBN 1-4251-0474-6
Printed in Victoria, BC, Canada

Printed on paper with minimum 30% recycled fibre. Trafford's print shop runs on "green energy" from solar, wind and other environmentally-friendly power sources.

TRAFFORD
PUBLISHING

Offices in Canada, USA, Ireland and UK

This book was published *on-demand* in cooperation with Trafford Publishing. On-demand publishing is a unique process and service of making a book available for retail sale to the public taking advantage of on-demand manufacturing and Internet marketing. On-demand publishing includes promotions, retail sales, manufacturing, order fulfilment, accounting and collecting royalties on behalf of the author.

Book sales for North America and international:
Trafford Publishing, 6E–2333 Government St.,
Victoria, BC v8t 4p4 CANADA
phone 250 383 6864 (toll-free 1 888 232 4444)
fax 250 383 6804; email to orders@trafford.com

Book sales in Europe:
Trafford Publishing (UK) Limited, 9 Park End Street, 2nd Floor
Oxford, UK ox1 1HH UNITED KINGDOM
phone 44 (0)1865 722 113 (local rate 0845 230 9601)
facsimile 44 (0)1865 722 868; info.uk@trafford.com

Order online at: trafford.com/06-2231

10 9 8 7 6 5 4 3 2

To my very special grandkids who inspired this book, and hopefully many more.

Big Red Ants don't wear pants...

but give them a chance and

Ants are quite small
and not very tall...

But
they can
climb up
a wall
and
not ever
...fall.

On the sides
of their heads,
Ants have eyes
that are BLACK.

They can see where they've been
Without looking back....

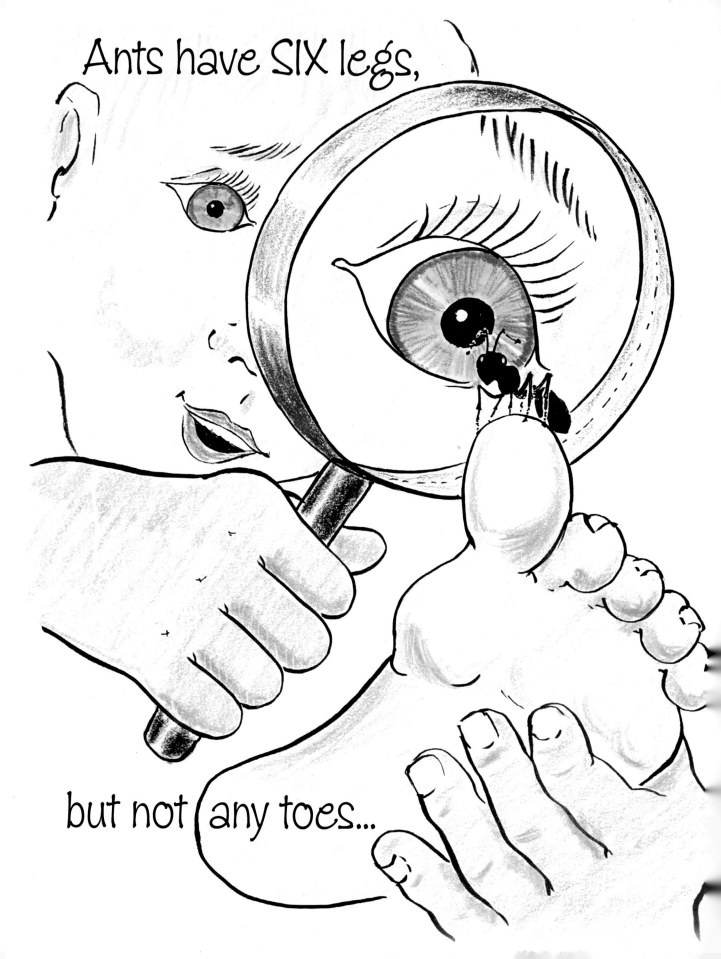

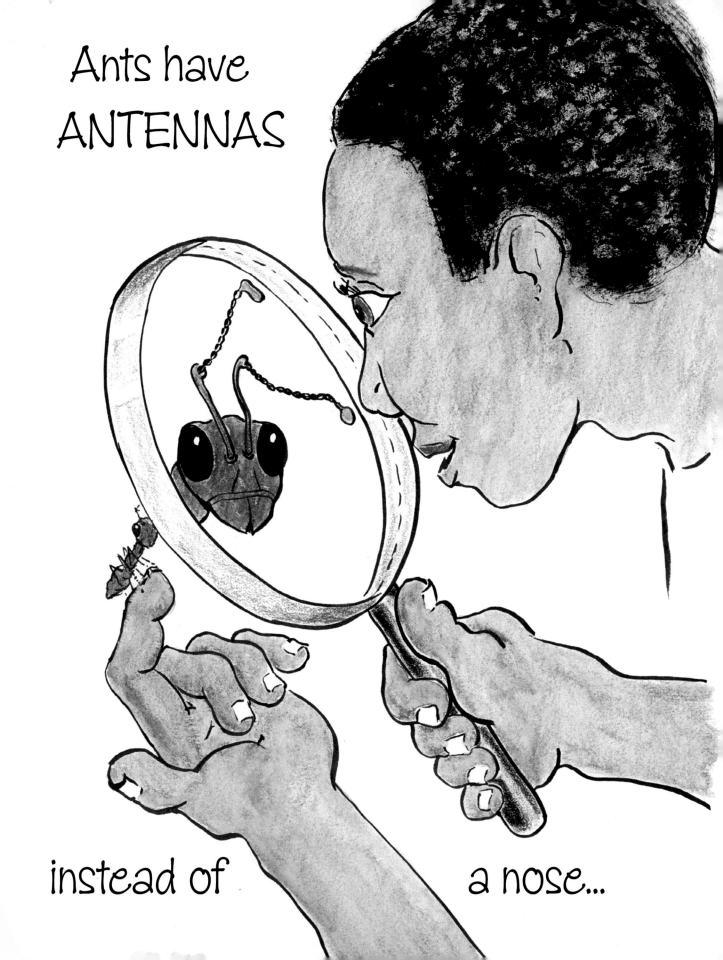

Ants have ANTENNAS

instead of

a nose...

Some ants might bite you.
And some ants might sting.

If you play on an ant's nest

you will know
what I
mean...

Ants are smart bugs.

They keep their homes clean...

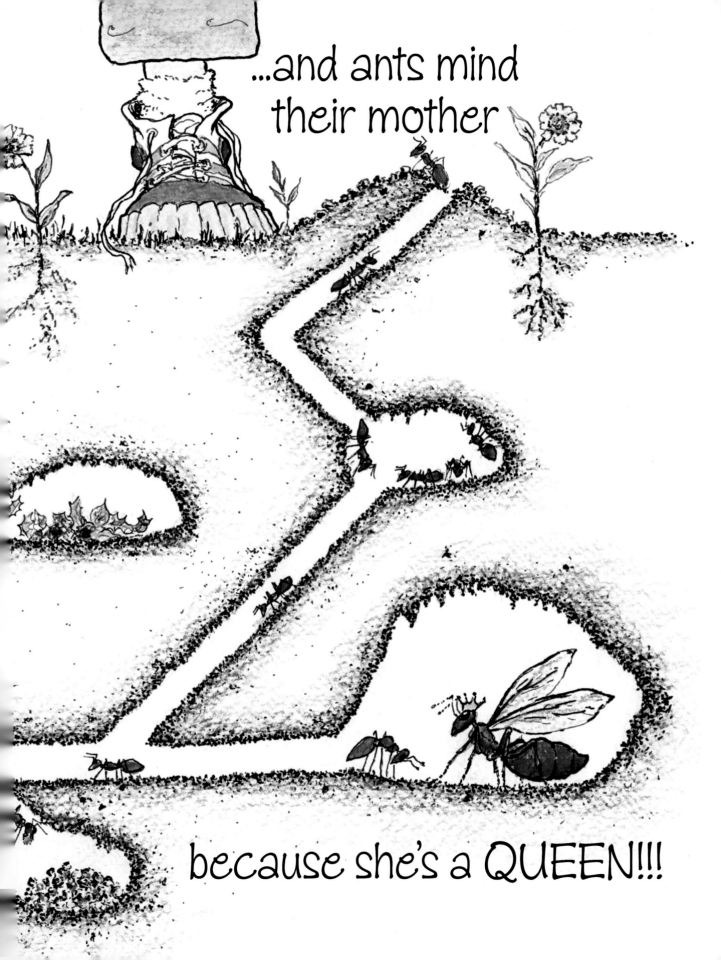

Ants are good neighbors
They work very hard.

We think you are
GREAT Ants

But PLEASE
stay out in the yard...

Ants don't wear pants,
but what if they DID!!!

Do you think they would look
like any other KID??

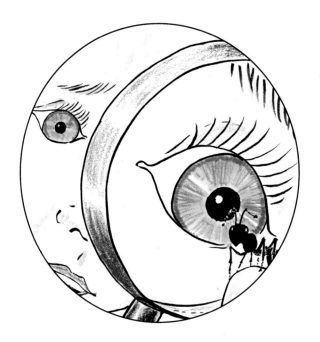

THE END

...but not for long.